You Can, Toucan

by Jenny Jinks

illustrated by
Amy Zhing

It was time for Toucan to learn
to fly.

He stepped out of the nest
and flapped his wings.

"I cannot do it!" Toucan said.

"You can, Toucan," said his mum.
"Have another go."

Toucan spread his wings wide.

He flapped and flapped.

Up he went.

"I CAN do it!" he said.

Toucan went to play hide and seek with Monkey.

But his beak was too big and bright.

"I cannot do it!" Toucan said.

"You can, Toucan," said Monkey.
"Have another go."

Toucan hid in the branches
of a tree. Monkey did not see him.

"I CAN do it!" said Toucan.

Next, Toucan went to swim in the river.

He dipped his foot in.

But it was too cold and deep.

"I cannot do it!" Toucan said.

"You can, Toucan," said Fish.

"Have another go."

Toucan splashed in the river.

He swam all the way across.

"I CAN do it!" said Toucan.

It was time for the jungle party.

Toucan wanted to join in and dance.

He began to tap his feet.

"I cannot…" Toucan began,
but he stopped and said,
"I CAN!"

He swirled and twirled.

BANG! CRASH!

"I can do it!" said Toucan.

"I can dance!"

"No, Toucan, you cannot!"

the others said.

Toucan felt sad.

"But you will be good at dancing soon," they said. "Have another go!"

Quiz

1. What did Toucan usually say?
a) "I might do it!"
b) "I will not do it!"
c) "I cannot do it!"

2. What advice did everyone give?
a) "Give up."
b) "Have another go."
c) "Try something else."

3. What did Toucan find hard about hide and seek?
a) Monkey was cheating
b) His feathers were too dark
c) His beak was too big and bright

4. What did Toucan find hard about the river?
a) It was too cold and deep
b) It was too fast
c) It was too dirty

5. What did Toucan do at the party?
a) Sing
b) Dance
c) Play hide and seek

Turn over for answers

Book Bands for Guided Reading

The Institute of Education book banding system is a scale of colours that reflects the various levels of reading difficulty. The bands are assigned by taking into account the content, the language style, the layout and phonics. Word, phrase and sentence level work is also taken into consideration.

Maverick Early Readers are a bright, attractive range of books covering the pink to white bands. All of these books have been book banded for guided reading to the industry standard and edited by a leading educational consultant.

To view the whole Maverick Readers scheme, visit our website at
www.maverickearlyreaders.com

Or scan the QR code above to view our scheme instantly!

Quiz Answers: 1c, 2b, 3c, 4a, 5b